Save
Pudding Wood

Written by Roderick Hunt
Illustrated by Nick Schon,
based on the original characters
created by Roderick Hunt and Alex Brychta

OXFORD
UNIVERSITY PRESS

Read these words

pudding　　good

foot　　hook

could　　bush

would　　should

Chip and Craig went to Pudding Wood.
Craig's dad took them.

Craig loved Pudding Wood. He was good at seeing birds and animals.

"I can see a woodpecker," said Craig.
"Look. It's up in that tree."

"Look," said Craig. "Can you see that deer? It's by that bush."

"Sssh! Keep still," said Craig's dad.
"Look at the foot of that big tree.
It's a treecreeper."

I can *see* it!

They met Wilma and her dad.
Wilma had bad news.

"It's Pudding Wood," she said.

"They want to chop it down and put up houses."

They ran back as fast as they could.

"It's bad news," said Chip. "They want to cut down Pudding Wood."

Could they do that?

"Could they?" said Biff.

"Would they?" said Mum.

"They couldn't," said Gran.

"I think they could," said Wilma's dad.

"It would be really bad to chop down Pudding Wood," said Mum.

They wouldn't do it, would they?

"Well, can we stop them?" said Gran.

"We could call a meeting," said Craig.

They had a meeting in the hall.
The hall was full.

Craig's dad made a speech.

"We must stop them by hook or by crook," he said.

"Look at my photos of
Pudding Wood," said Craig.

"It has bluebells . . .

. . . and deer,

. . . and lots of birds.
I love Pudding Wood."

They all gave Craig a cheer.
"Let's go to the Town Hall,"
called a man.

That would be good.

"We could make a big banner and take it with us," said a woman.

The next day they all went to
the Town Hall. Mum had made a
big banner.

Craig had made a banner, too. He put it on his wheel-chair.

At last there was good news.

Pudding Wood was saved.

"I should think so, too," said Biff.
"The birds and animals need
Pudding Wood."

"We need Pudding Wood too,"
said Craig.

Talk about the story

Which one?

The 'oo' sound can be spelled *oo, oul* or *u*. Can you choose the correct spelling for these words? Look back in the story to check if you are right.

w___d

w___d

p__dding

sh___d

g___d